Book One

TITAN BOOKS

INTRODUCTION

At the beginning of the Franco Prussian war, the French writer Gustave Flaubert said, of those about to fight, something to the effect of 'All that is certain is that they will be just as stupid when it's over.'

Just as stupid and just as likely to fight again. It seems the only thing war teaches people is how to fight wars more effectively. And if war itself cannot change this human stupidity, what chance then has a novel or a film or even a comic?

No chance, obviously. But these were the thoughts that were moping around my mind after Steve MacManus and Simon Geller, erstwhile editorial team of *2000 AD*, had asked me to write a story called *Bad Company*. *Bad Company* had originally been devised by the little-known writing duo, John Wagner and Alan Grant, for inclusion in the *Judge Dredd Comic*. The *Dredd* comic was planned as an alternative title to *2000 AD*, featuring Judge Dredd. Unfortunately, nothing came of the plans for the new comic but editors Steve and Simon wanted a gutsy future war story like *Bad Company* in the regular *2000 AD*.

Originally, *Bad Company* had been devised as part of the Dredd mythos, featuring a Judge who had turned bad and had been shipped off to a prison colony located on Titan, one of Saturn's moons. I dropped all these aspects of the story, but kept the basic premise of a group of fresh-faced raw recruits confronted by a band of war-hardened renegades, fighting on a distant, inhospitable planet. From then on, the series' direction was down to me.

What interested me was not so much the fighting or the war itself. I was more interested in the effect that the war and the fighting were having on the raw recruits, Danny Franks, Trucker, Mac and the rest, and the change the war had already wrought on the members of Bad Company; in particular, Kano. I wanted to see how the recruits changed, and I wanted Danny Franks to know that Kano and his Bad Company cut-throats were the living embodiments of the change, of the dehumanization induced by this war and, by extension, all wars.

Again, futuristic weapons did not interest me much. I was more concerned with creating a kind of archetypal war scenario: horrible conditions; alien environment; an enemy known more through rumour and propaganda than fact, and a group of young men a long way from the 'home' for which they were meant to be getting themselves honourably slaughtered.

From the outset, I had intended that Danny and his friends' transition from the very human, raw and simple to their later hardened, more complex, and more twisted

condition should be reflected in the changing feel of the narrative and the look of the artwork. This, of course, required the right artistic team, and it was not until I was some way into the scripts that the artists whom I had wanted from the beginning, Brett Ewins and Jim McCarthy, volunteered for *Bad Company* duty. It quickly became an indivisible three-man project, with Brett and Jim's artwork achieving dimensions hitherto unseen in *2000 AD* future-war stories.

In conclusion, if Flaubert was right, and wars do not make people less stupid, it is vain to suppose that a story about war could. In this case the most I can hope for is that this particular future-war story does not make any of its readers *more* stupid.

Peter Milligan, *May 1987*

PETER MILLIGAN was born. But then again who wasn't. He took Fine Art at Goldsmiths College, and they're still waiting for him to give it back. His first published comics writing was The Electric Hoax, which appeared in Sounds Music Weekly. Subsequent scriblings included Sooner or Later, The Dead *and* Bad Company *for 2000AD, as well as the newspaper strip* Summer of Love *for The* News on Sunday. *In America, between 1983/1985 he created* Strange Days *with Brendan McCarthy and Brett Ewins and* Johnny Nemo *with Ewins for Eclipse Comics. He is currently working on a number of film projects, here and abroad. Other current projects include writing a second* Bad Company *series entitled* Kano in the Bewilderness *for 2000AD, as well as* Paradax *with Brendan McCarthy for Vortex Comics. Peter is writing a novel and he has a number of projects under negotiation with American comics publishers.*

BRETT EWINS left University with a B A in conceptual art and a desperate need to draw for money. He joined 2000AD in its first year and went on to illustrate Judge Dredd, Rogue Trooper *and* Judge Anderson, *among others. In America he has co-created* Strange Days *and* Johnny Nemo *magazines with Milligan. He has recently completed the first series of* Bad Company *for 2000AD; and* Mad Balls *for Marvel UK. He is currently drawing* Action Force *for Marvel UK, as well as the second* Bad Company *series for 2000AD. He is also negotiating new projects with DC Comics and the N M E.*

JIM McCARTHY burnt off vast amounts of energy playing drums and percussion in various reggae/latin/funk bands before entering the graphics business. He has worked as a cartoonist for various industrial training projects, as well as for book publishers such as Cassells, Mitchell Beazley, etc. He has also worked on film and advertising storyboards. Bad Company *is his first foray into the I P C world, and he brings a taut Ditko-esque finish to his work. He is currently working on the second* Bad Company *series.*

Published by Titan Books Ltd, 58 St Giles High St, London WC2H 8LH, England. Distributed in the United Kingdom and the United States of America by Titan Distributors Ltd, P.O. Box 250, London E3 4RT, England. *Bad Company* is © IPC Magazines Ltd, 1987. This edition is © Titan Books Ltd, 1987. Printed in England. ISBN 1 85286 020 0. *First edition August 1987.*

10 9 8 7 6 5 4 3 2

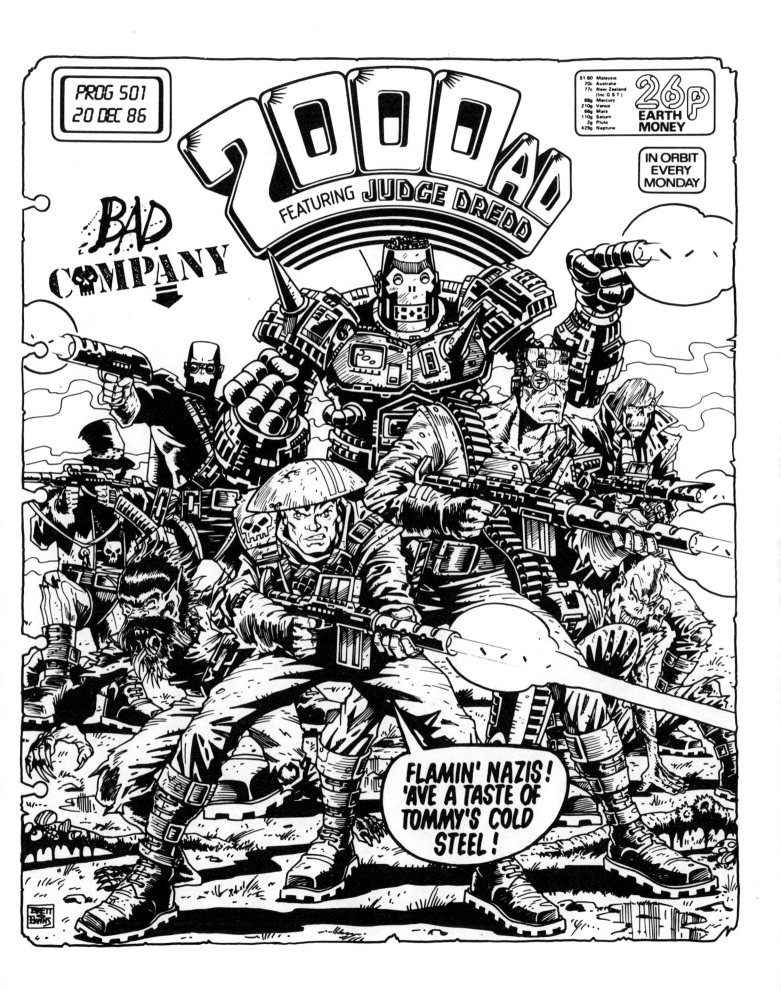

SCRIPT
PETE MILLIGAN

ART
EWINS/J. McCARTHY

LTG
TOM FRAME

ARARAT. 24.6.2210. My name is Daniel Franks. I am a soldier in the 1st Colony Division. Today I am going to die.

NOOOOOOOoooo

'Your planet needs you', they said, so we came to fight the Krool. Perhaps we all had our own reasons. Fear, anger, indoctrination...

NOooooOOOOO!

...guilt?

TEN HOURS THEY'VE BEEN SCREAMING, DANNY. WHAT ARE THEY DOING TO THEM?

IT'S CALLED TORTURE, TRUCKER. AND IT'S BEST NOT TO THINK ABOUT IT.

JUST DON'T LET KROOL TAKE YOU ALIVE.

ATTENTION, MEN! FOR THOSE OF YOU WHO DON'T KNOW, I'M PECK, YOUR NEW COMMANDER.

NOW, IF KROOL TAKE ARARAT, THEY WILL HAVE A BRIDGEHEAD FROM WHICH TO ATTACK EARTH ITSELF...

BAD COMPANY

...BUT WE ARE SURROUNDED. THIS SECTOR'S LOST — AND WE CAN ACHIEVE NOTHING BY CONTINUED RESISTANCE.

WE HAVE A DUTY TO SURVIVE. WE MUST LIVE TO FIGHT ANOTHER DAY.

WE MUST SURRENDER AND DEMAND OUR RIGHTS TO BE FAIRLY TREATED AS PRISONERS OF WAR.

PECK, YOU'RE PATHETIC. YOU STILL STINK OF MILITARY TRAINING SCHOOL.

HOW DARE —

DROP DEAD! THIS IS PROBABLY MY LAST DAY ALIVE.

I DON'T WANT YOUR VOICE TO BE THE LAST THING I HEAR.

THE WORD DUTY SHOULD BE SCRATCHED FROM THE LANGUAGE. ALONG WITH HONOUR.

AND YOU SHOULD'VE STAYED AT HOME, PECK. YOU'RE NOT FIGHTING HUMAN BEINGS.

"YOU'RE FIGHTING KROOL..."

THEY'RE NOT RENOWNED FOR LISTENING TO REASON...

AIIEE!

"KROOL OPERATE ON DEAD SOLDIERS, GIVING THEM SOME KIND OF DEMENTED HALF LIFE — TURNING THEM INTO MONSTROUS PUPPETS, PROGRAMMED TO KILL LIVING HUMANS..."

"WAR ZOMBIES!"

8

Suddenly, they were all around us. And something about them seemed more decayed and rotten than the War Zombies. These really were the living dead...

LOOK AT THE SNIVELLING SWINE. NO WONDER KROOL ARE WINNING... LET'S **BURY** THEM, LADS!

NO.

SOME OF THEM MIGHT BE **USEFUL**.

I'M IN COMMAND HERE. WHO ARE **YOU**?

WHAT DIVISION DO YOU BELONG TO? WHERE ARE YOUR PAPERS?

DID YOU HEAR THAT? THE **COMMANDER** WANTS TO KNOW WHO WE ARE!

WE'RE THE **NIGHTMARE** DIVISION, BOY...

PLIK!

THE NEXT MAN WHO **ANNOYS** ME GETS FED TO **DOGBRAIN**. UNDERSTOOD?

THAT'S THE **THING** I SAW ATTACKING THE WAR ZOMBIES!

I'VE HEARD RUMOURS ABOUT THIS OUTFIT...

...ABOUT **RENEGADES** WHO OPERATE BEHIND KROOL LINES — LED BY A MAN WHO'S **MADDER THAN KROOL!**

THAT'S **KANO**, DANNY...

9

INTO THE CLEARING!

AND DON'T TURN BACK UNLESS YOU'RE TIRED OF LIVING!

THEY'RE...THEY'RE USING US AS BAIT! **HUMAN** BAIT!

On Earth, people used to dig hooks into worms. The hooks were on the end of a line, and the line was cast into the water. When a fish swallowed the worm it swallowed the hook too...
'Fishing' was banned some years ago. They said it was cruel to the fish. For the first time in my life, I decided I was on the side of the worm.

I THOUGHT KANO WAS BETTER THAN THE OTHERS – BUT HE'S WORSE!

WHAT'S WORSE, TRUCKER? BEING HOOKED OR BEING SWALLOWED?

I'M **SICK** OF YOUR FANCY CHAT, FRANKS! IF YOU'RE SO **SMART**, WHAT ARE YOU DOING IN A **KROOL-FODDER DIVISION** LIKE **THIS**?

SHUT UP, JONES! YOU'LL GET US ALL...

GRUUUH!

FDDANNGG!

KROOL AMBUSH! FORM A SQUARE, MEN – GIVE THEM A TASTE OF **EARTH GRIT**!

Sometimes the fish were so hungry for the worm they'd swallow not only the baited hook, but the lead weight and some of the line as well.

14

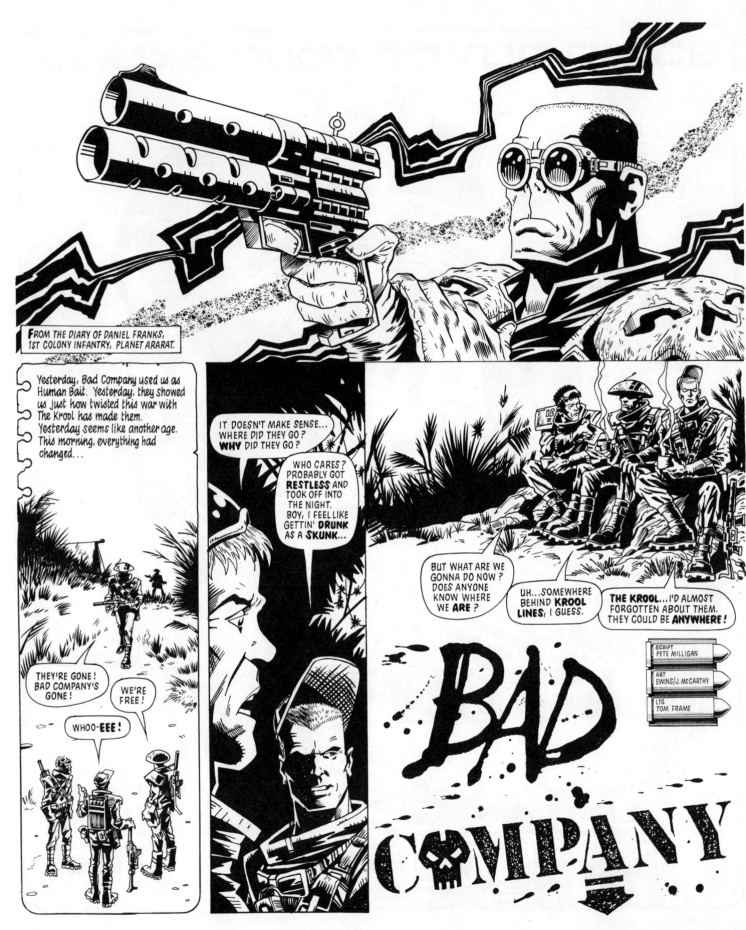

FROM THE DIARY OF DANIEL FRANKS, 1ST COLONY INFANTRY, PLANET ARARAT.

Yesterday, Bad Company used us as Human Bait. Yesterday, they showed us just how twisted this war with The Krool has made them. Yesterday seems like another age. This morning, everything had changed...

THEY'RE GONE! BAD COMPANY'S GONE!

WE'RE FREE!

WHOO-EEE!

IT DOESN'T MAKE SENSE... WHERE DID THEY GO? WHY DID THEY GO?

WHO CARES? PROBABLY GOT RESTLESS AND TOOK OFF INTO THE NIGHT. BOY, I FEEL LIKE GETTIN' DRUNK AS A SKUNK...

BUT WHAT ARE WE GONNA DO NOW? DOES ANYONE KNOW WHERE WE ARE?

UH...SOMEWHERE BEHIND KROOL LINES, I GUESS.

THE KROOL...I'D ALMOST FORGOTTEN ABOUT THEM. THEY COULD BE ANYWHERE!

BAD COMPANY

SCRIPT
PETE MILLIGAN

ART
EWINS/J. McCARTHY

LTG
TOM FRAME

26

For ten hours now, Krool have been spraying this area with random scatter-bombs. So we're cooped-up in a Blitz Bubble, a semi-organic inflatable 'shell' that can withstand just about anything except a direct hit...

SCRIPT
PETE MILLIGAN

ART
EWINS/J. McCARTHY

LTG
TOM FRAME

BAD COMPANY

WHOMP!

AND IT'S ENOUGH TO DRIVE ANYONE CRAZY...

♪ THERE'LL BE BLUE BIRDS OVER ♪ — DON'T BE SHY, LADS — ♪ THE WHITE CLIFFS OF DOVER ♪♪

GRUB UP!

TASTY SLIME-FLEAS!

YOU'RE TENSE. BOMBS GETTING TO YOU?

NO, I'M THINKING ABOUT ALL THE **NORMAL PEOPLE** I KNEW ON **EARTH**... WONDERING IF I'LL EVER SEE THEM AGAIN.

SURE. WE'RE ON OUR OWN. WITH NO WAY HOME...

KANO SAYS EARTH IS DYING... SAYS THE EARTH SELECT ARE GOING TO SELL US OUT. IS IT TRUE?

SO WHY ARE WE FIGHTING?

WHY NOT? MAYBE WE'LL **BEAT** KROOL. MAYBE SOME OF US WILL **SURVIVE.**

MAYBE WE'LL STOP THE SELECT TAKING OVER.

THAT'S A LOT OF MAYBES.

WHOMP

WHUMP

MAYBE IT IS...

GET OFF, DOGBRAIN! PLAY **DEAD** OR SOMETHING!

ONLY EVER LISTENS TO **KANO** – DAMN ANIMAL!

WHAT IS IT WITH THAT CREATURE? HE'S MADDER THAN MAD TOMMY...

...AND THAT'S SAYING SOMETHING!

Y'SEE, SHRIKE, **THE NAZIS** WAS MOVING THEIR **PANZERS** UP HERE... BUT THEY RECKONED WITHOUT THE OLD **DUNKIRK SPIRIT,** DIDN'T THEY?

NEXT: **THE VALE OF TEARS**.

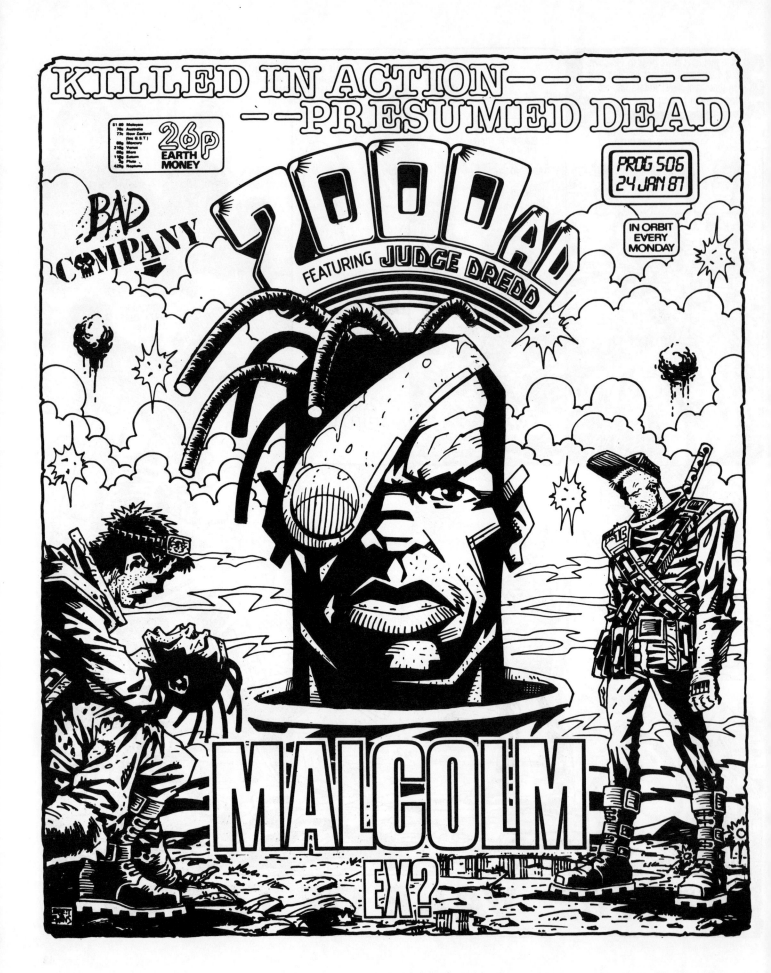

48

49

DID YOU EVER MEET TED AND CHRIS, MY BROTHERS? THEY JOINED UP BEFORE ME... BOTH DIED WHEN THEIR TRANSPORT SHIP TO ARARAT EXPLODED.

THE ARMY SAID IT WAS AN "UNFORTUNATE MECHANICAL FAILURE"!

THAT'S ALL GONE NOW, DANNY. EARTH, HOME, FIREBOWL GAMES... ALL GONE...

THE BLUES LOST—24:16— BUT ALL WE COULD THINK ABOUT WAS OUR **EARTH DEAD** ROTTING ON AN ALIEN PLANET...

NEXT: *ZOMBIE BEAT!*

MAAAAAAA

THE ZOMBIES ARE FLAKING OUT!

AND **DOGBRAIN'S** STOPPED WHINING.

I THINK HE'S HUNGRY...

ON YOUR BELLIES! KROOL!

We lay by the stinking corpses and played dead. There were only four Krool. Two were Fang-Faces. I guessed the others were scientists, showing off their handiwork...

60

THE END.